A CHILD OF OUR TIME

Oratorio for soli, chorus and orchestra
with text and music by

MICHAEL TIPPETT

Vocal Score

SCHOTT & CO. LTD. LONDON

48 Great Marlborough Street, London, W1V 2BN

B. Schott's Söhne, Mainz

Schott Music Corporation, New York

". . . the darkness declares the glory of light"

Soprano, Contralto, Tenor and Bass soloists,

Chorus (S A T B)

ORCHESTRA

2 Flutes
2 Oboes
Cor Anglais
2 Clarinets
2 Bassoons
Double bassoon
4 Horns
3 Trumpets
3 Trombones
Timpani and Cymbals (1 Player)
Strings

Approximate duration: Part I, 24 mins., Part II, 24 mins.,
Part III, 18 mins.

CONTENTS

Part I

NOTES

If a large choir is used care should be taken in those choruses (Nos. 3, 5, etc.) which are lightly scored, that a single line of voices (Sopranos, Altos, etc.) should balance the solo wood-wind (1 Bassoon or 1 Oboe, etc.). The number of voices singing should be reduced accordingly.

The recitatives should be sung in *tempo,* and at about the speed at which they would be spoken.

The spirituals should not be thought of as congregational hymns, but as integral parts of the Oratorio; nor should they be sentimentalised but sung with a strong underlying pulse and slightly 'swung'. The consonants should not be over-distinct (*an'* rather than *and,* etc.).

A CHILD OF OUR TIME

An Oratorio for Soli, Chorus and Orchestra

PART I
No. 1 Chorus

MICHAEL TIPPETT

No. 2 The Argument

Alto Solo

8

Tru-ly, Tru-ly the liv-ing God con-sumes _____ with-in, _____ and turns the flesh, _____ and turns the flesh _____ to _____ can- - - cer!

Interludium

No. 3 Scena
Chorus and Alto Solo

* Vocalised with a repeated *hi*: wi-hi-hind.

*See note page 13.

16

(8va ad lib.)

No. 4 The Narrator
Bass Solo

No. 5 Chorus of the Oppressed

20

24

attacca

No. 6 Tenor Solo

-tween the ham - mer and the an - vil. I am caught be-

-tween my de - sires and their frus - tra - tion as be tween the ham - mer and the

an - vil. How can I grow

to a man's sta-ture? How can I grow,

can I grow to a man's, a man's

28

No. 7 Soprano Solo

No. 8 A Spiritual

Chorus and Soli

1. { My Lord, He calls me, He calls me by the thun-der,
2. { Green trees a-bend-ing, poor sinner stands a trem bling } The trumpet sounds with-

Ah ha ha ha _____

Ah ha ha ha _____

The trumpet sounds with-

The trumpet sounds with-

Brass

61

Ah___ Ah _____

(lunga)
in-a my soul, I han't got long to stay here. Steal___ a-way,

(lunga)
I han't got long to stay here. Steal___ a-way,

(lunga)
I han't got long to stay here. Steal___ a-way,—

(lunga)
in a my soul I han't got long to stay here. Steal___ a-way,

(lunga)
in a my soul I han't got long to stay here. Steal___ a-way, —

(lunga)

Dal 𝄋

End of Part I

PART II
No. 9 Chorus

No. 10 The Narrator
Bass Solo

No. 11 Double Chorus of Persecutors and Persecuted

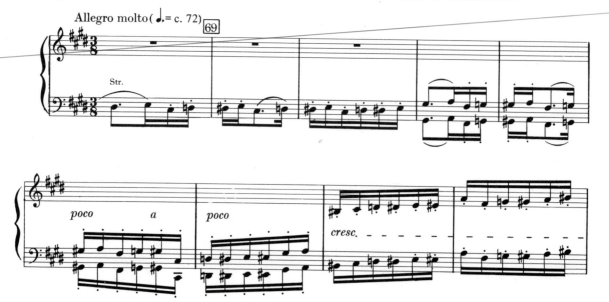

42

44

No. 12 The Narrator
Bass Solo

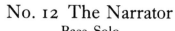

No. 13 Chorus of the Self-righteous

48

No. 14 The Narrator
Bass Solo

No. 15 Scena
The Mother, the Uncle and Aunt, and the Boy
Solo Quartet

segue

No. 16 A Spiritual
Chorus and Soli

No. 17 Scena
Duet — Bass & Alto

56

segue

No. 18 The Narrator
Bass Solo

No. 19 The Terror
Chorus

58

Burn down their hou-ses! Beat in their heads!

hou-ses! Beat in their heads! Break them in pie-ces on the wheel!

Burn! Beat! Break! Break them in pie -

Break them! Break them!

in pie-ces on the wheel!

- ces on the wheel! Burn down their

No. 20 The Narrator
Bass Solo

Men were a - shamed of what was done.

There was bit-ter-ness and ___ hor-ror.

segue

No. 21 A Spiritual of Anger
Chorus and Bass Solo

Go down, Mos - es, Way down in

Go down, Mos - es, Way down in

Go down, Mos - es, Way down in

Go down, Mos - es, Way down in

No. 22 The Boy Sings in his Prison
Tenor Solo

No. 23 The Mother
Soprano Solo

What have I done to you, my son?

What have I done to you, my son? What will be-come ___ of us now, ___ will be - come ___ of us now? The springs of hope, of hope ___

No. 24 Alto Solo

No. 25 A Spiritual

Chorus and Soprano Solo

End of Part II

PART III
No. 26 Chorus

No. 27 Alto Solo

- ioned like a wom-an.

115

f stacc.

dim.

p

Cor. Anglais

pp W.W.

p

She is old ——— as the earth,

Answered by ob.+ W.W.

116

She is old _____ as the earth, be-yond good and

ev-il, good and ev-il, the sens — — ual

gar-ments.

Her face _____ will be ill-um — —

Then __ is the time _____ of

his de- liv - er-ance.

No. 28 Scena
Bass Solo and Chorus

88

Andante poco più mosso

Tempo primo
Bass Solo

The man of des - tin - y is cut off___ from fel - low-ship.

Heal - - - - ing springs from the womb___ of time.

92

Tempo primo
Bass Solo

He, too, is out-cast, _____ his man - hood brok - en

in the clash ____ of powers. God o - ver powered him, the

child ____ of our time.

Preludium

No.29 General Ensemble
Chorus and Soli

98

No. 30 A Spiritual
Chorus and Soli

104

108

End of Part III

S & Co. 5150